HARD-Fi :
STARS OF CCTV

WISE PUBLICATIONS
part of The Music Sales Group
London / New York / Paris / Sydney / Copenhagen / Berlin / Madrid / Tokyo

PUBLISHED BY
WISE PUBLICATIONS,
8/9 FRITH STREET, LONDON, W1D 3JB, ENGLAND.

EXCLUSIVE DISTRIBUTORS:
MUSIC SALES LIMITED,
DISTRIBUTION CENTRE, NEWMARKET ROAD, BURY ST EDMUNDS,
SUFFOLK, IP33 3YB, ENGLAND.

MUSIC SALES PTY LIMITED,
120 ROTHSCHILD AVENUE, ROSEBERY,
NSW 2018, AUSTRALIA.

ORDER NO. AM983488
ISBN 1-84609-210-8
THIS BOOK © COPYRIGHT 2005 BY WISE PUBLICATIONS,
A DIVISION OF MUSIC SALES LIMITED.

MUSIC ARRANGED BY MATT COWE AND MARTIN SHELLARD.
MUSIC PROCESSED BY PAUL EWERS MUSIC DESIGN.
EDITED BY DAVID WESTON.

PRINTED IN THE UNITED KINGDOM.

WWW.MUSICSALES.COM

CASH MACHINE

WORDS & MUSIC BY RICHARD ARCHER

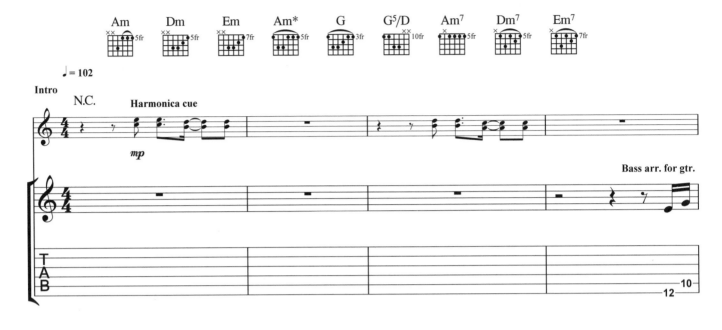

Verse

1. Go to a cash ma-chine, to get a tick-et home. A mes-sage on the screen
2. I try to phone a friend, my cre-dit's in the red. I try to skip the fare,
3. What am I gon-na do, my girl-friend's test turned blue. We tried to play it safe,

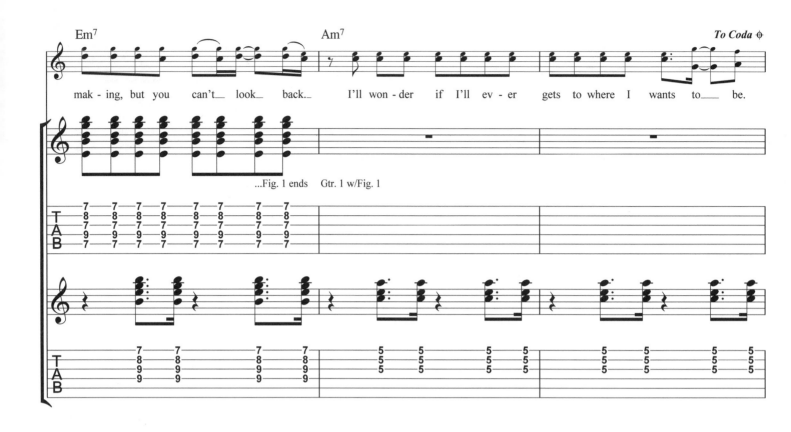

mak - ing, but you can't look back.. I'll won - der if I'll ev - er gets to where I wants to be.

...Fig. 1 ends   Gtr. 1 w/Fig. 1

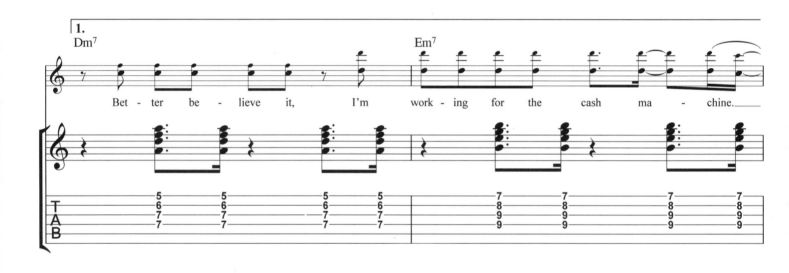

1.

Bet - ter be - lieve it, I'm work - ing for the cash ma - chine.

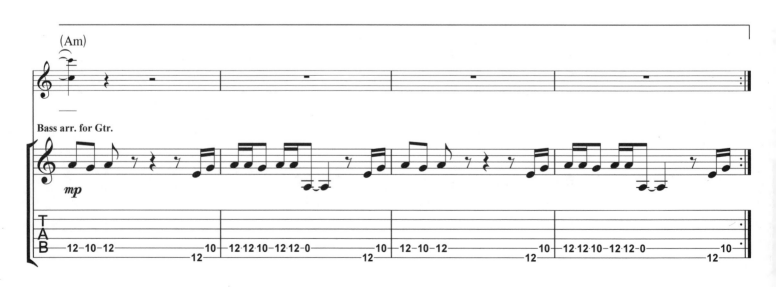

(Am)

Bass arr. for Gtr.

6

MIDDLE EASTERN HOLIDAY

WORDS & MUSIC BY RICHARD ARCHER

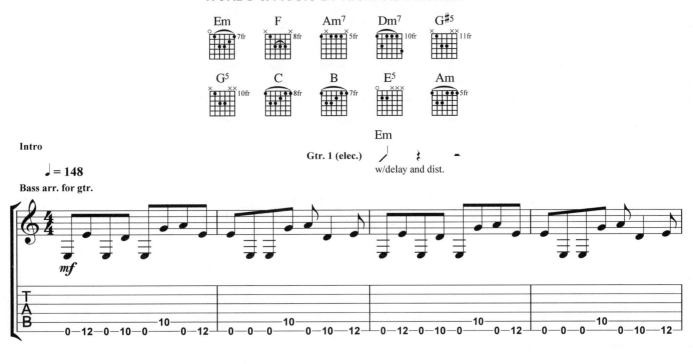

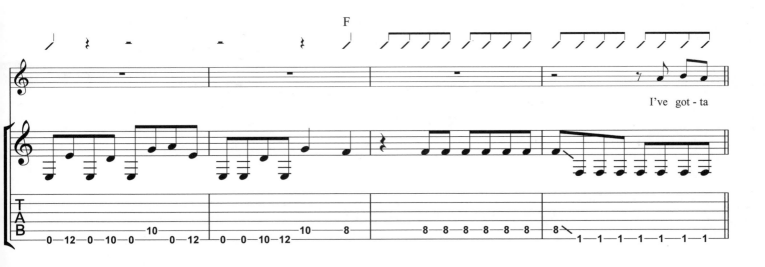

I've got-ta

go, (got-ta go, got-ta go, got-ta go,) but what a prize to give.

(2.) one, (twen-ty one, twen-ty one, twen-ty one,) and mean-while back at home,

(3.) gun, (got a gun, got a gun, got a gun,) bul-lets meant for me.

9

(Oh,   oh,   oh.) A pack-age deal to the sun, ev-'ry-thing is in-clu-sive.___
(oh,   oh,   oh, oh,) my friends are out to-night all drink-ing and danc-ing.___
(Oh,   oh,   oh, oh.) Time seems to stand still, I'm so scared I can't speak.___

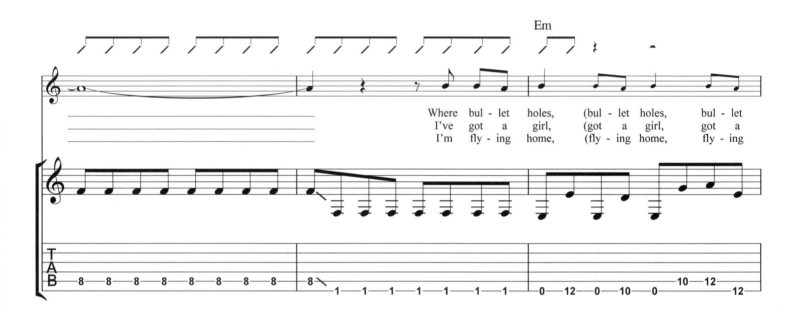

Where bul-let holes, (bul-let holes, bul-let
I've got a girl, (got a girl, got a
I'm fly-ing home, (fly-ing home, fly-ing

holes, bul-let holes) scar the mi-na-rets, (oh, oh, oh, oh,) smoke
girl, got a girl,) is she miss-ing me? (Oh, oh, oh, oh.)
home, fly-ing home) a-bove ev-'ry-thing, (oh, oh, oh, oh,) I

10

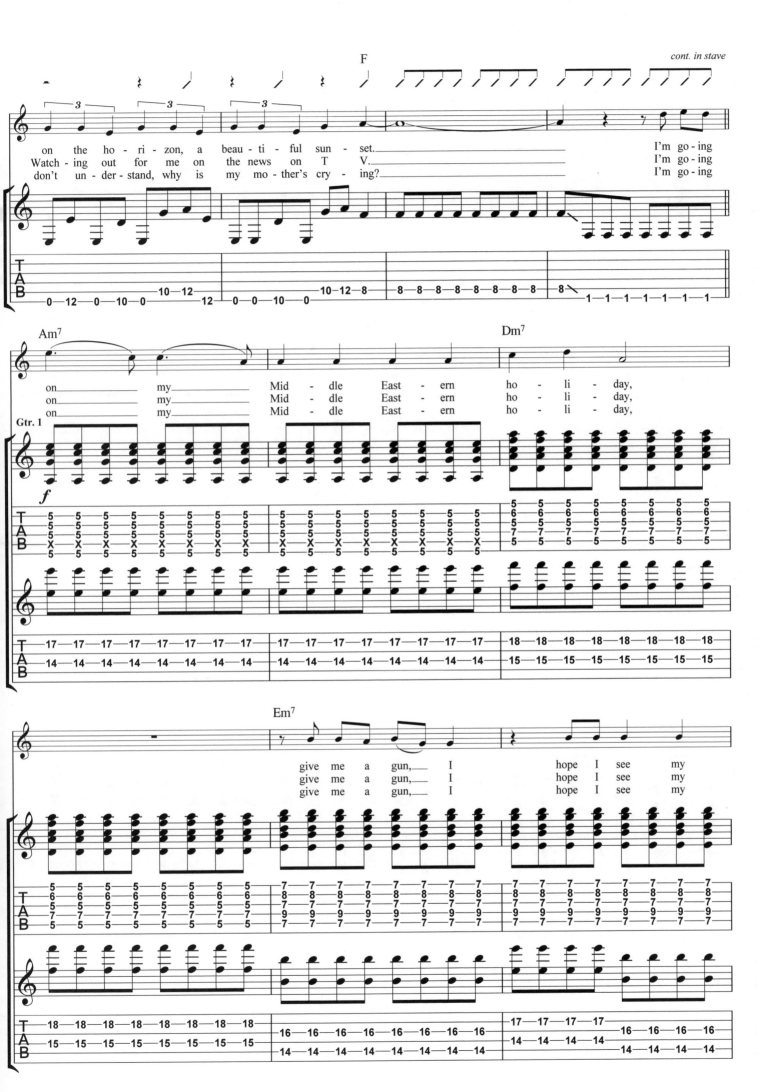

cont. in stave

11

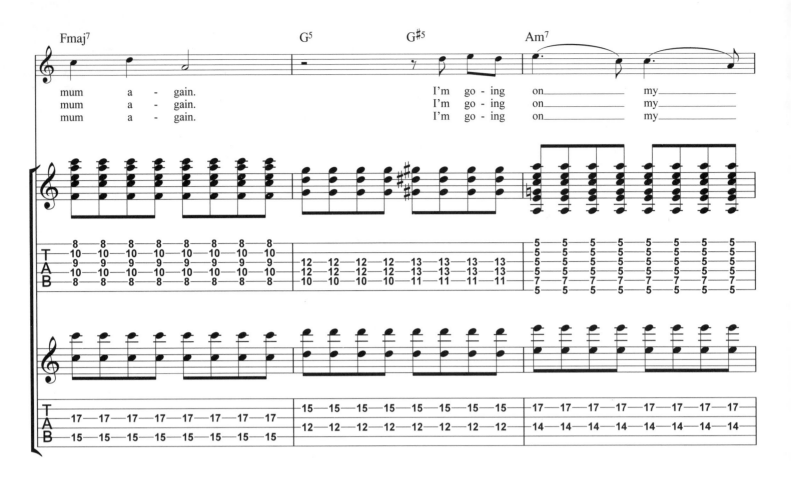

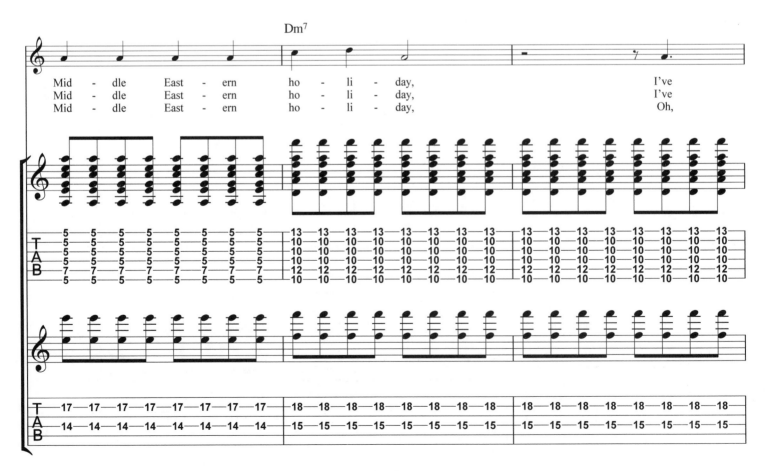

13

14

TIED UP TOO TIGHT

WORDS & MUSIC BY RICHARD ARCHER

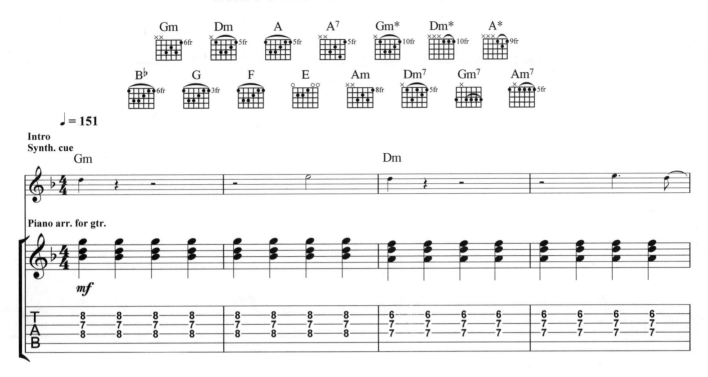

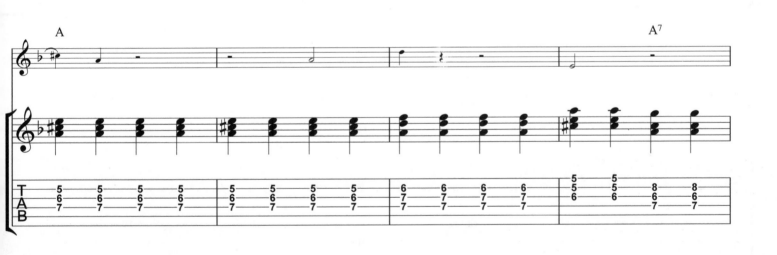

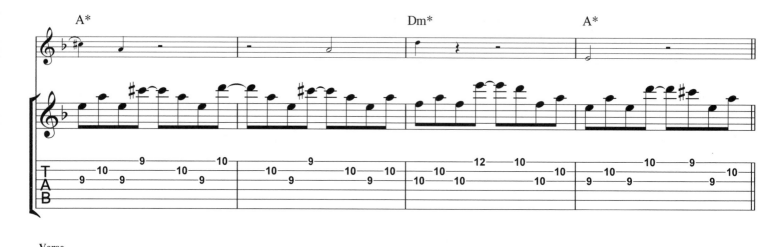

Verse

1. Oh where___ I come_ from,_____ I just___don't con - form,

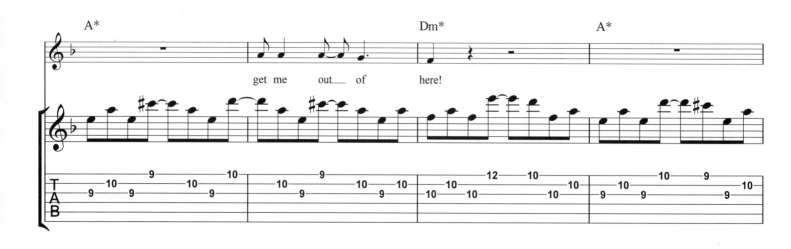

get me out___ of here!

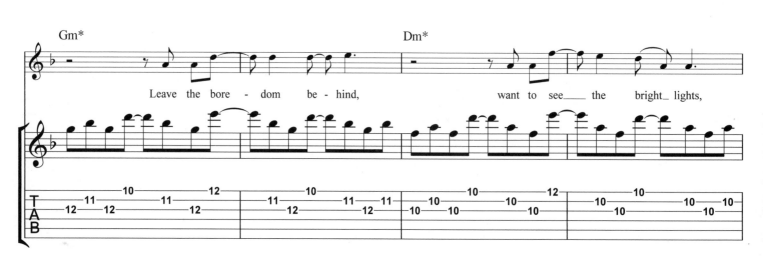

Leave the bore - dom be - hind, want to see___ the bright_ lights,

18

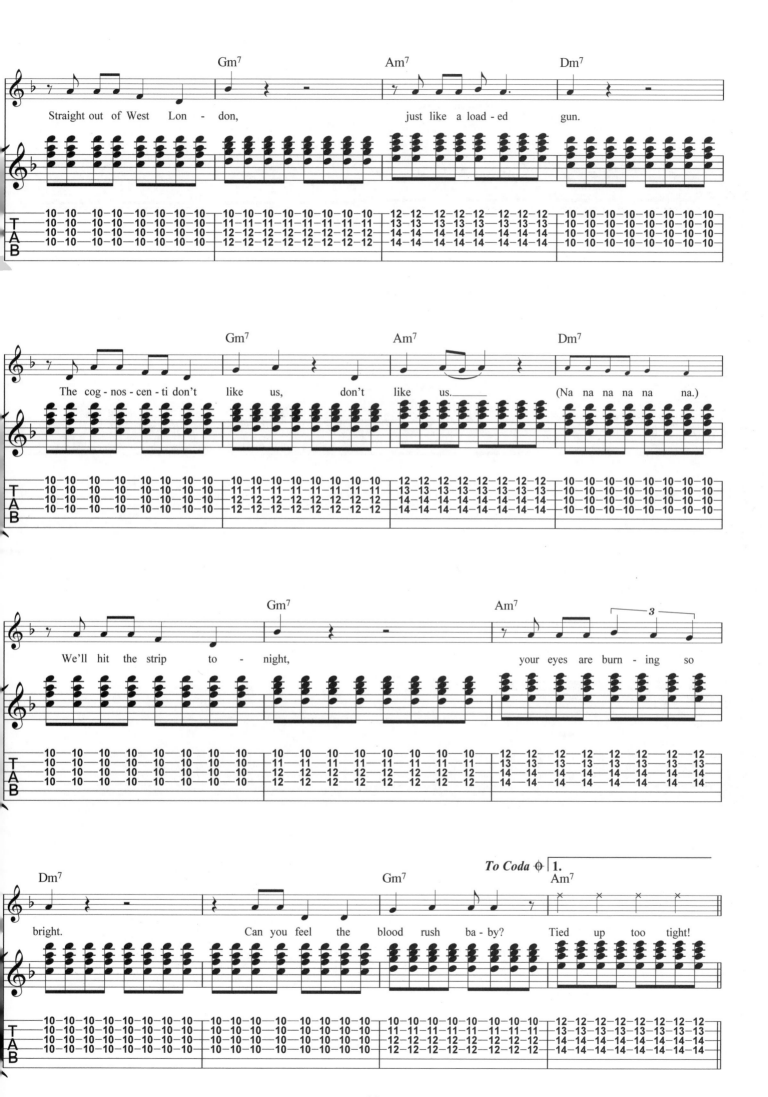

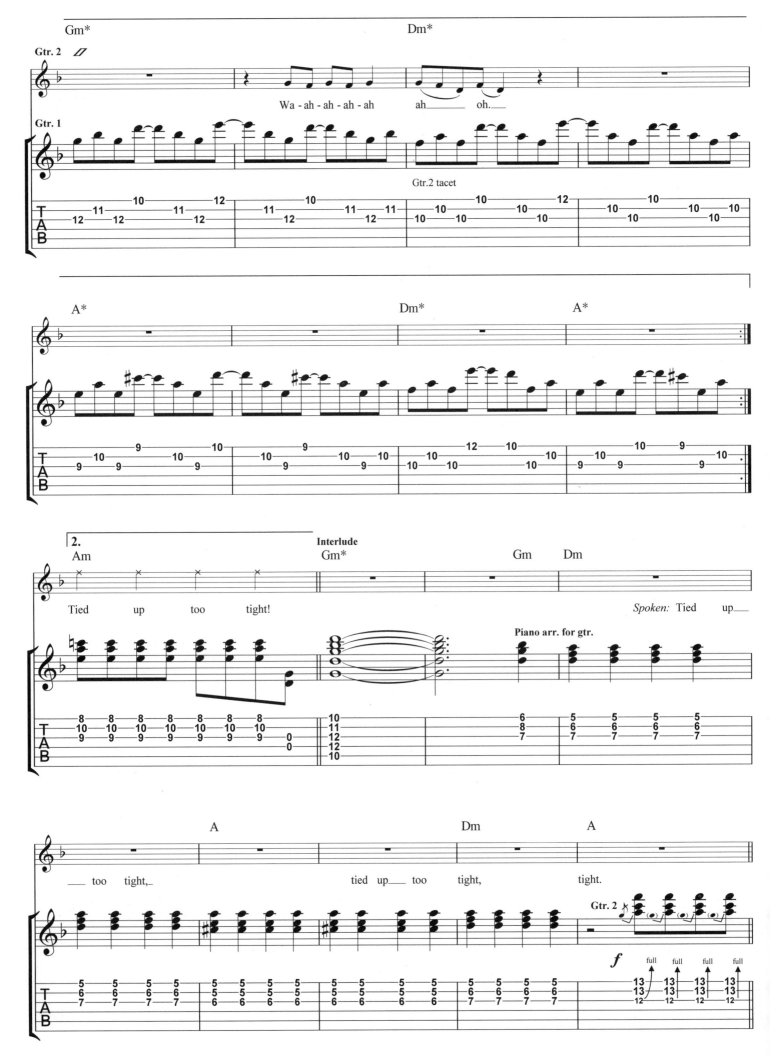

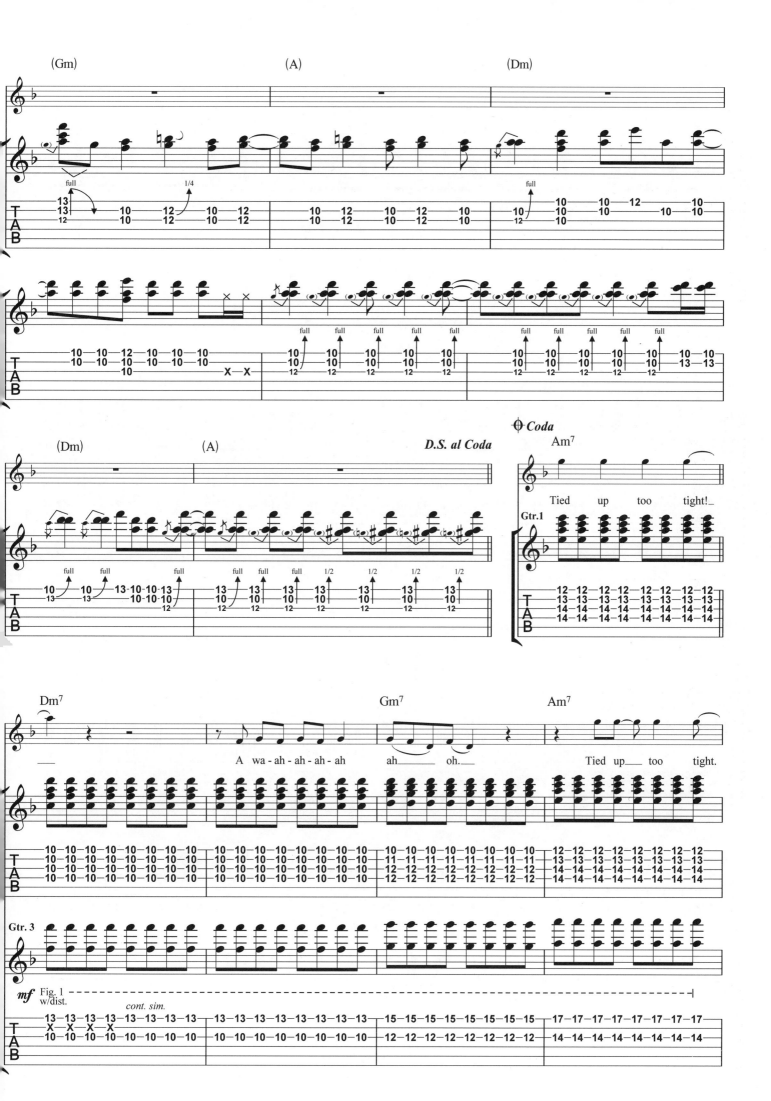

21

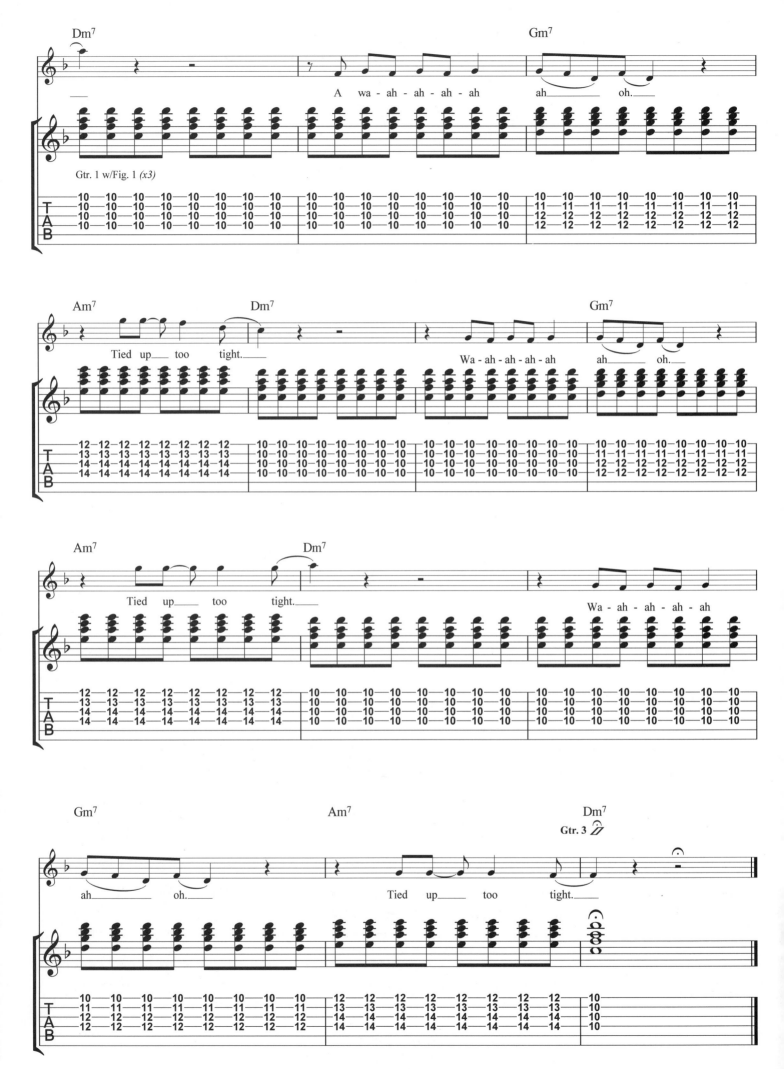

GOTTA REASON

WORDS & MUSIC BY RICHARD ARCHER

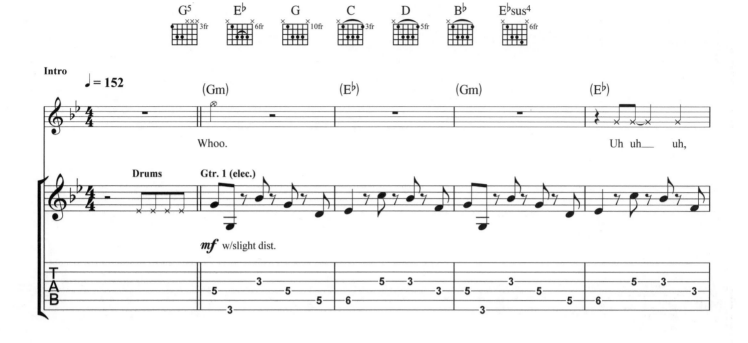

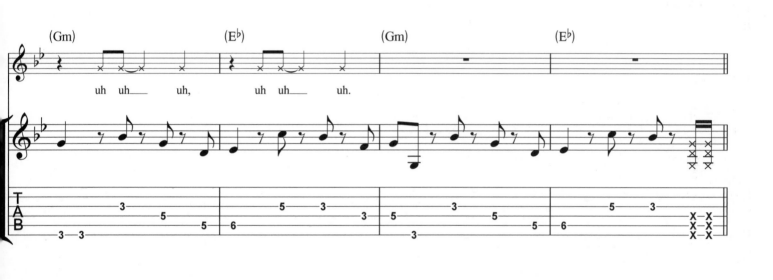

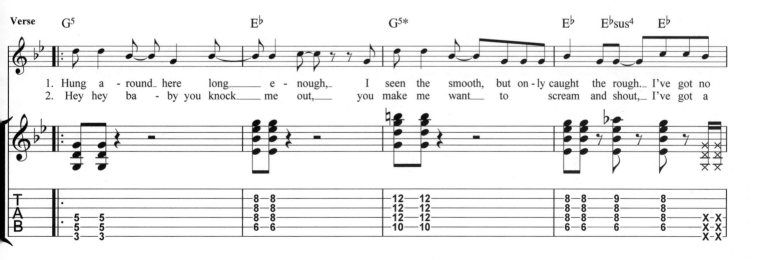

24

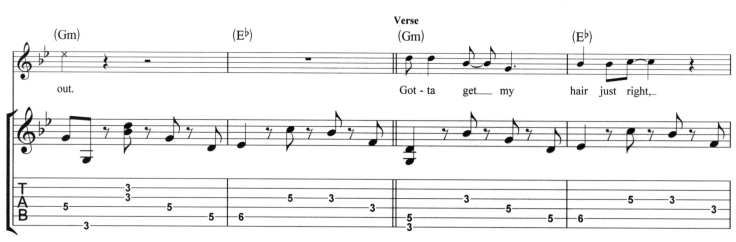

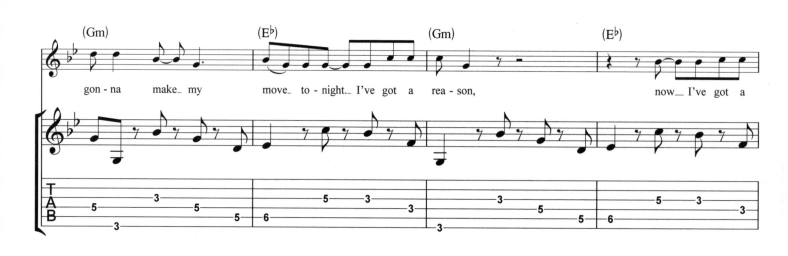

HARD TO BEAT

WORDS & MUSIC BY RICHARD ARCHER

29

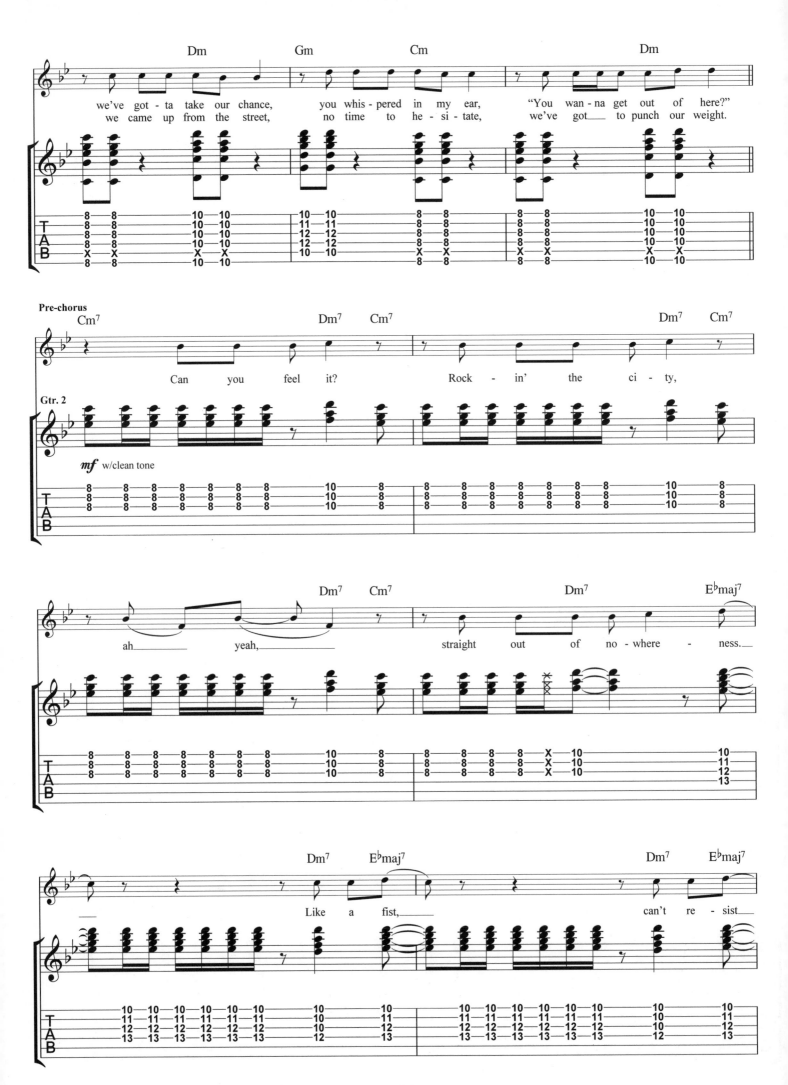

UNNECESSARY TROUBLE

WORDS & MUSIC BY RICHARD ARCHER

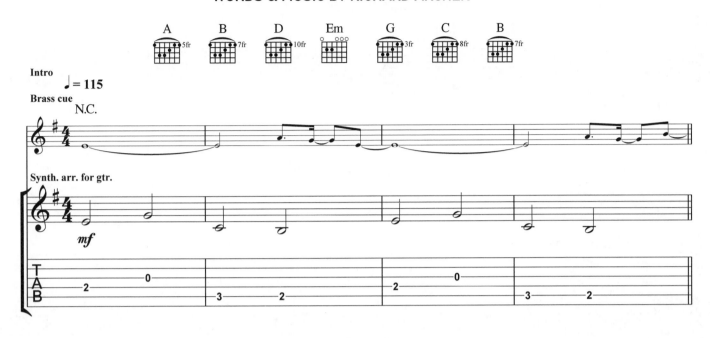

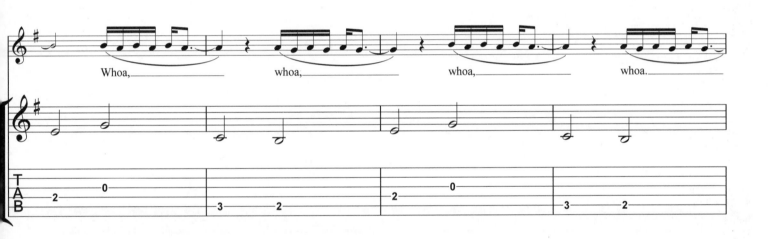

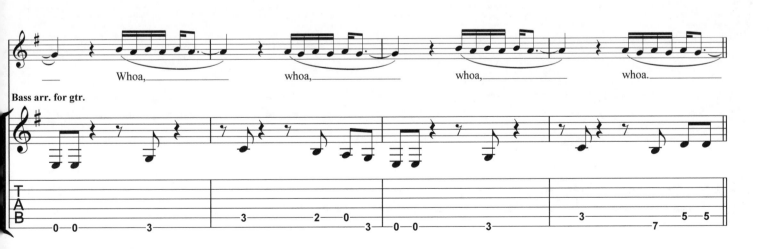

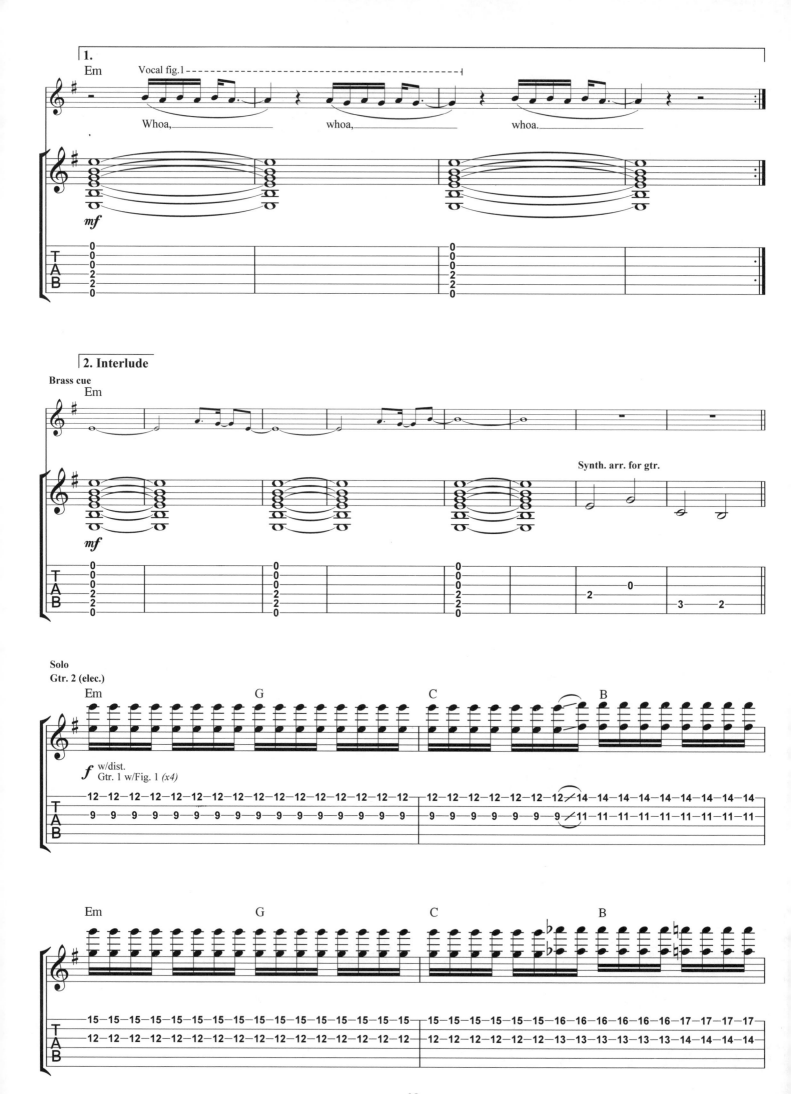

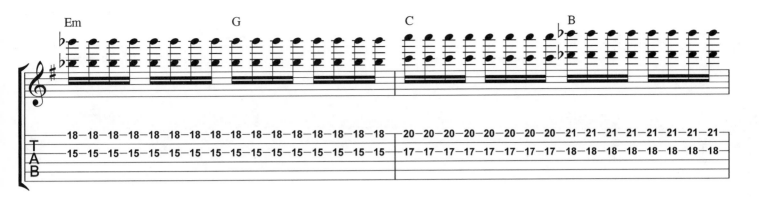

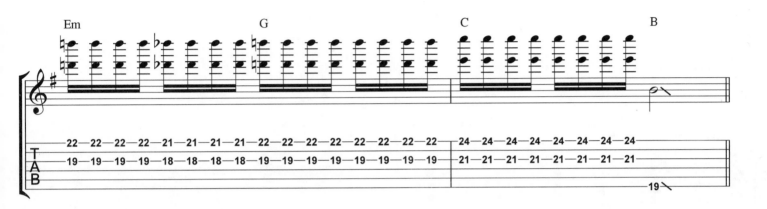

Chorus

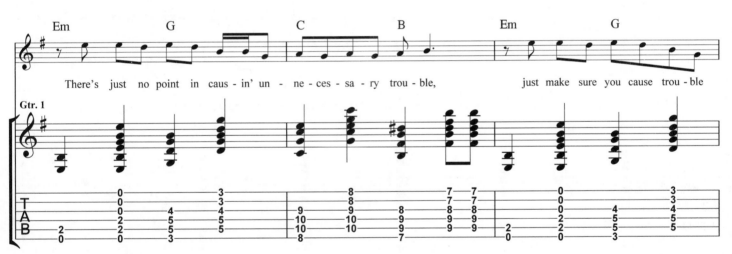

There's just no point in caus-in' un - ne - ces - sa - ry trou - ble, just make sure you cause trou - ble

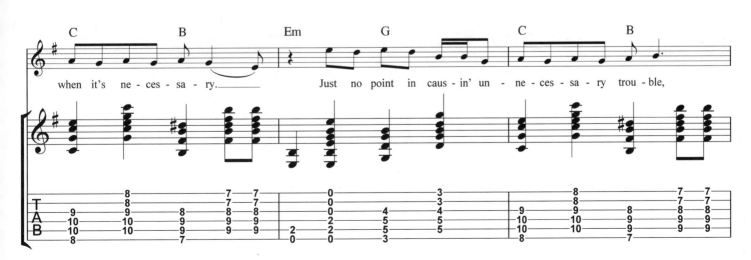

when it's ne - ces - sa - ry._____ Just no point in caus - in' un - ne - ces - sa - ry trou - ble,

MOVE ON NOW

WORDS & MUSIC BY RICHARD ARCHER

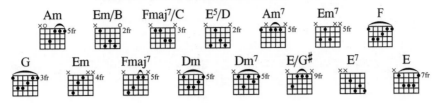

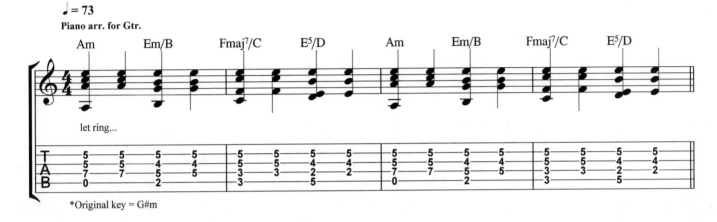

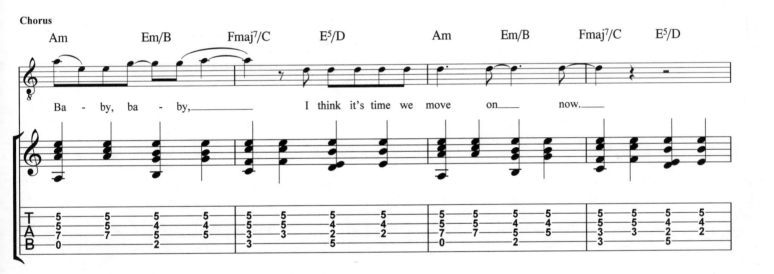

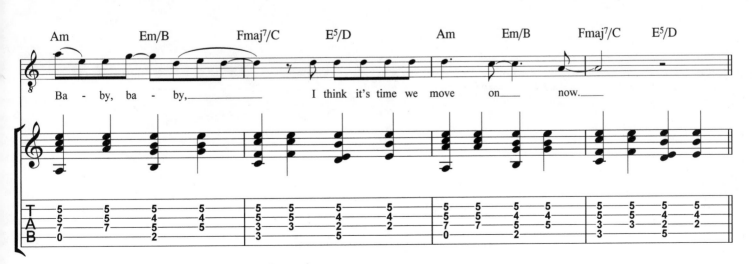

44

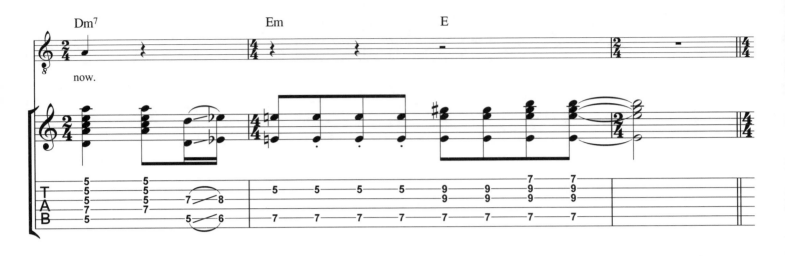

Outro

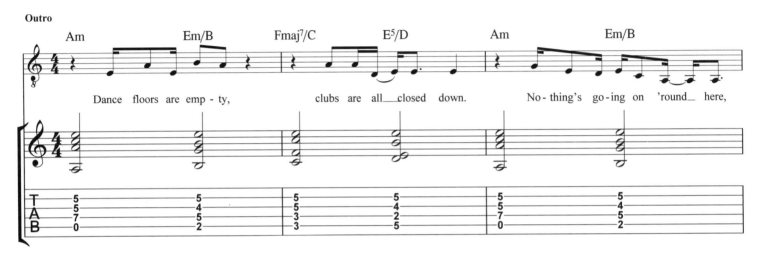

Dance floors are emp - ty, clubs are all closed down. No - thing's go - ing on 'round here,

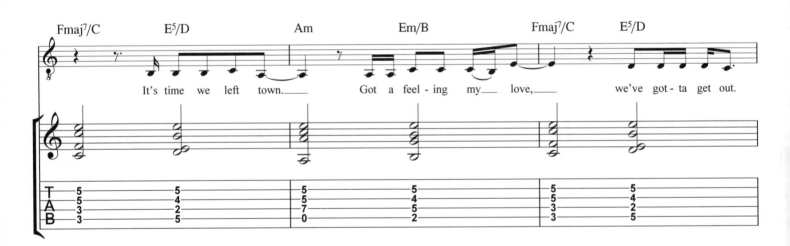

It's time we left town. Got a feel - ing my love, we've got - ta get out.

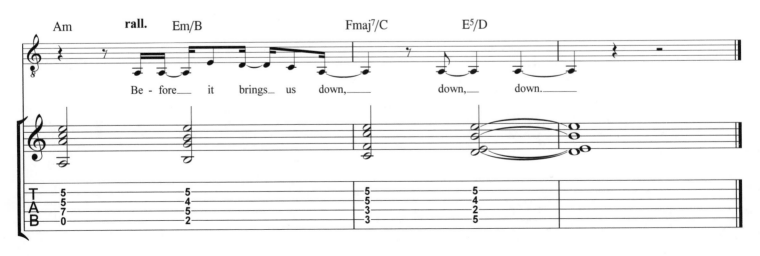

Be - fore it brings us down, down, down.

BETTER DO BETTER

WORDS & MUSIC BY RICHARD ARCHER

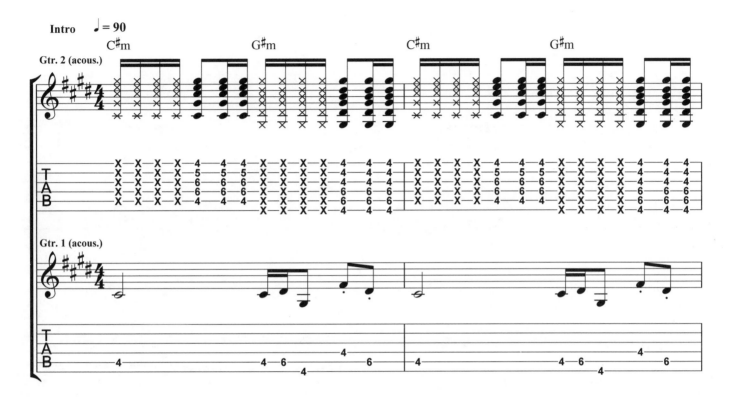

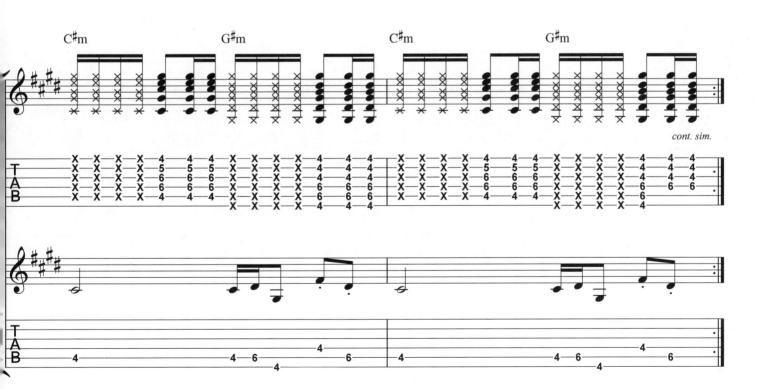

Verse

1. You're back, sit - ting on my door - step. Oh yeah, like no - thing hap - pened.
2. Your face makes me wan - na be sick. Oh yeah, it's a phy - si - cal re - ac - tion.

Gtr. 3 (elec.)

mf w/clean tone

cont. sim.

Tell - ing me that you're free and oh,_____ can you see me a - gain?
You'd bet - ter leave 'cos you see I can't_____ won't be blamed for my ac - tions.

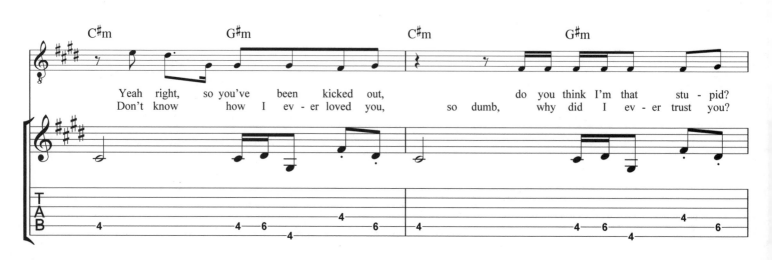

Yeah right, so you've been kicked out, do you think I'm that stu - pid?
Don't know how I ev - er loved you, so dumb, why did I ev - er trust you?

51

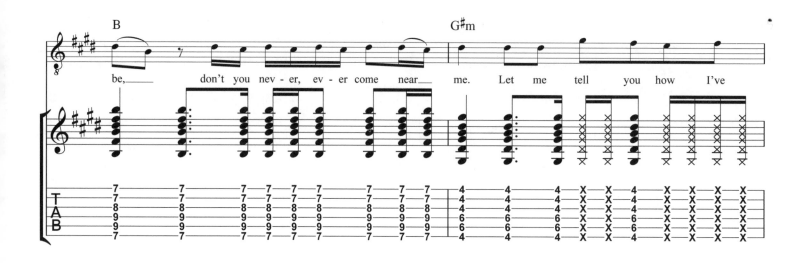

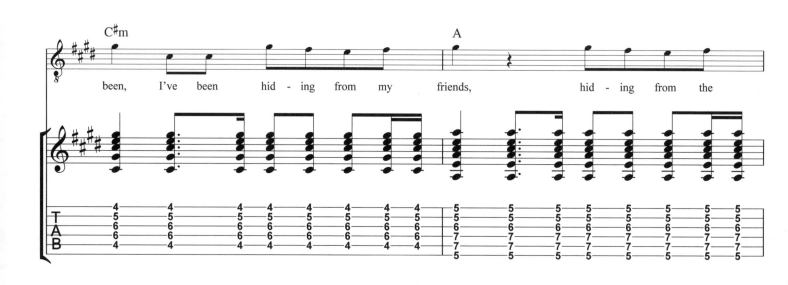

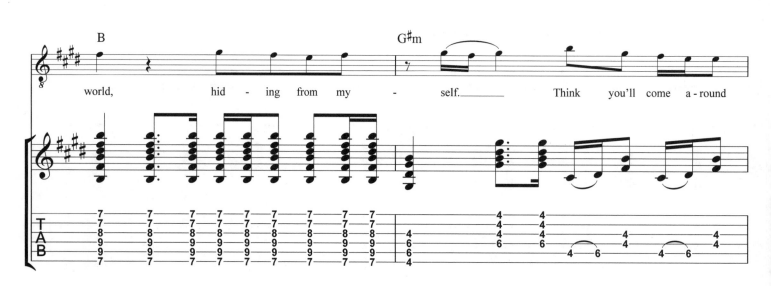

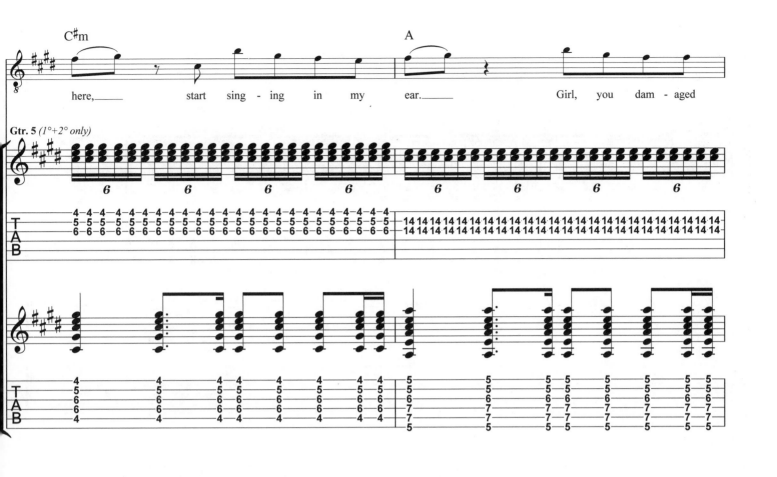

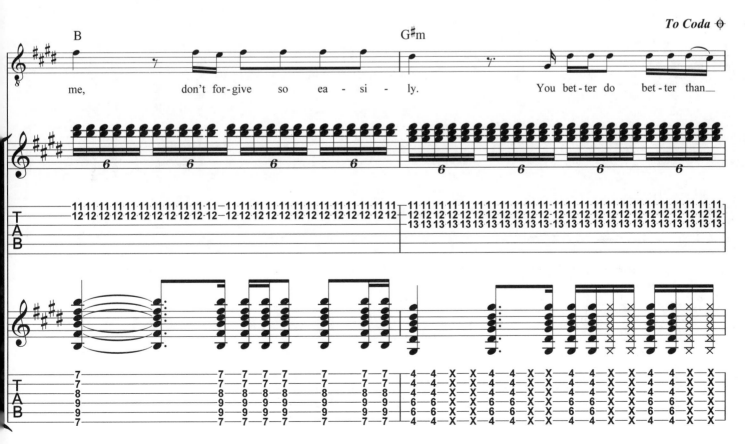

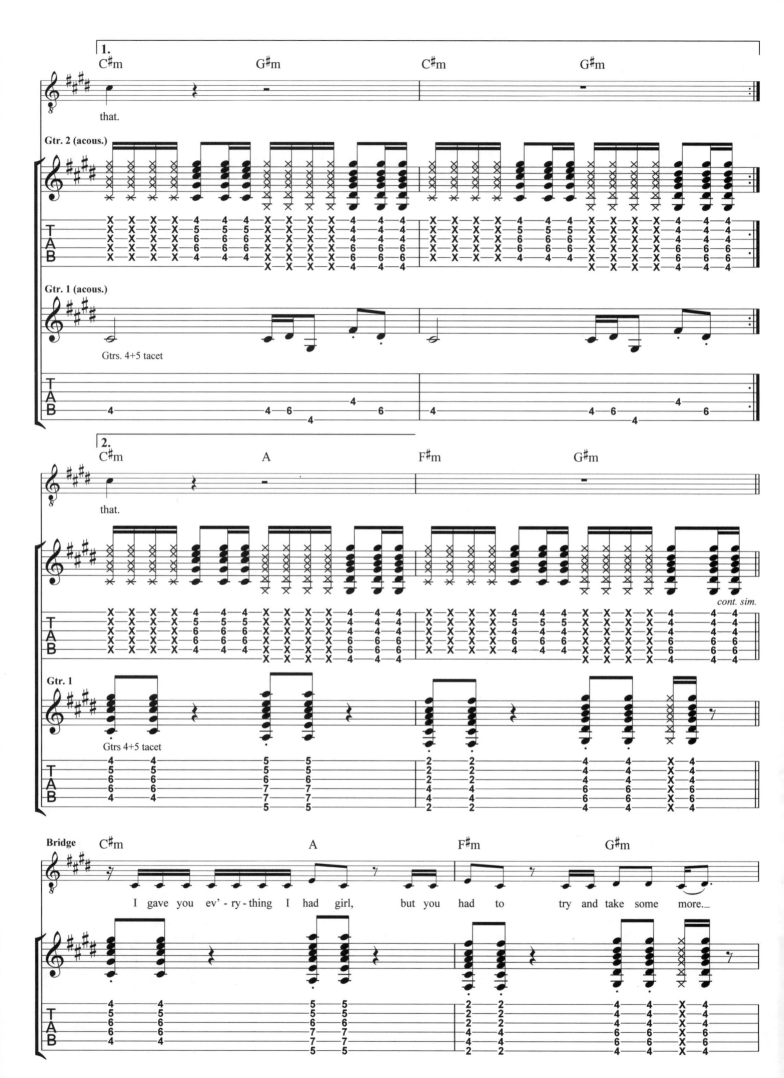

54

55

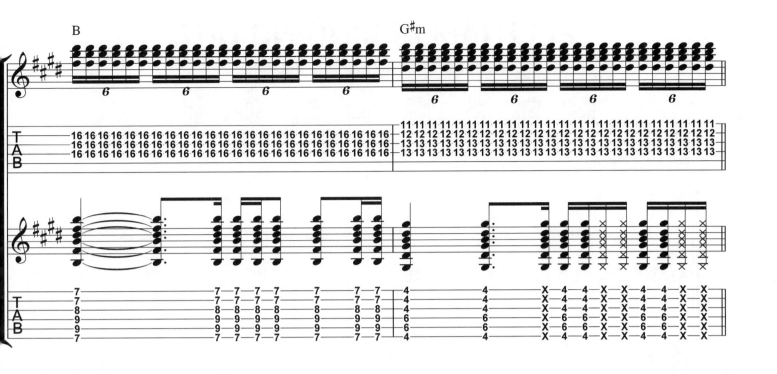

Outro

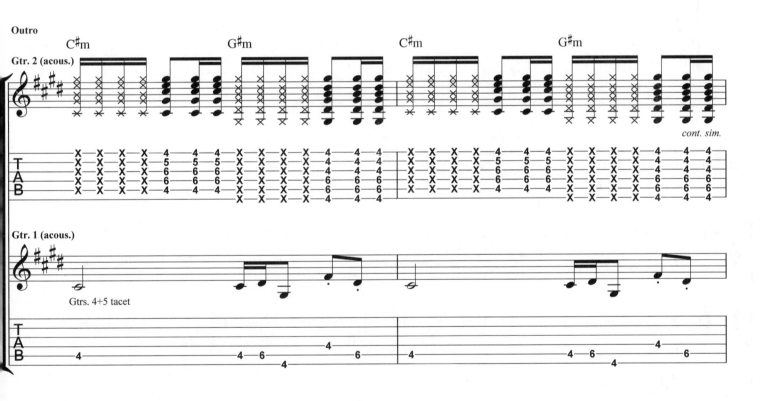

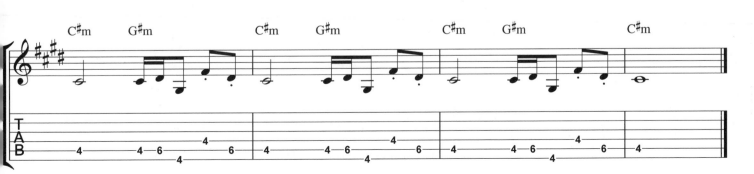

FELTHAM IS SINGING OUT

WORDS & MUSIC BY RICHARD ARCHER

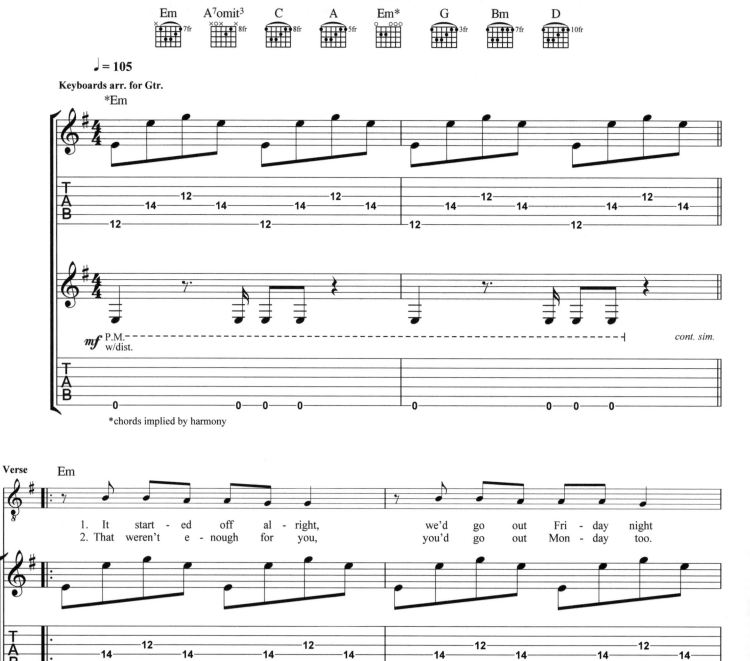

Em   A⁷omit3   C   A   Em*   G   Bm   D

♩ = 105

Keyboards arr. for Gtr.

*Em

mf P.M.
w/dist.

cont. sim.

*chords implied by harmony

Verse   Em

1. It start- ed off al- right,   we'd go out Fri- day night
2. That weren't e- nough for you,   you'd go out Mon- day too.

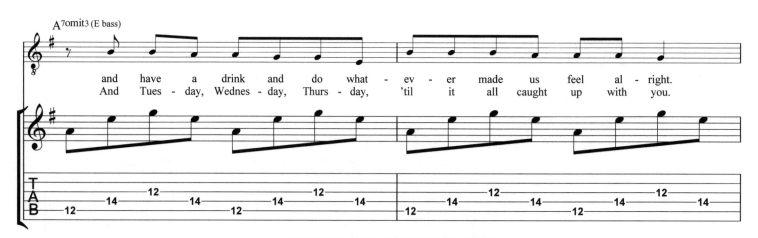

A⁷omit3 (E bass)

and have a drink and do what- ev- er made us feel al- right.
And Tues- day, Wednes- day, Thurs- day, 'til it all caught up with you.

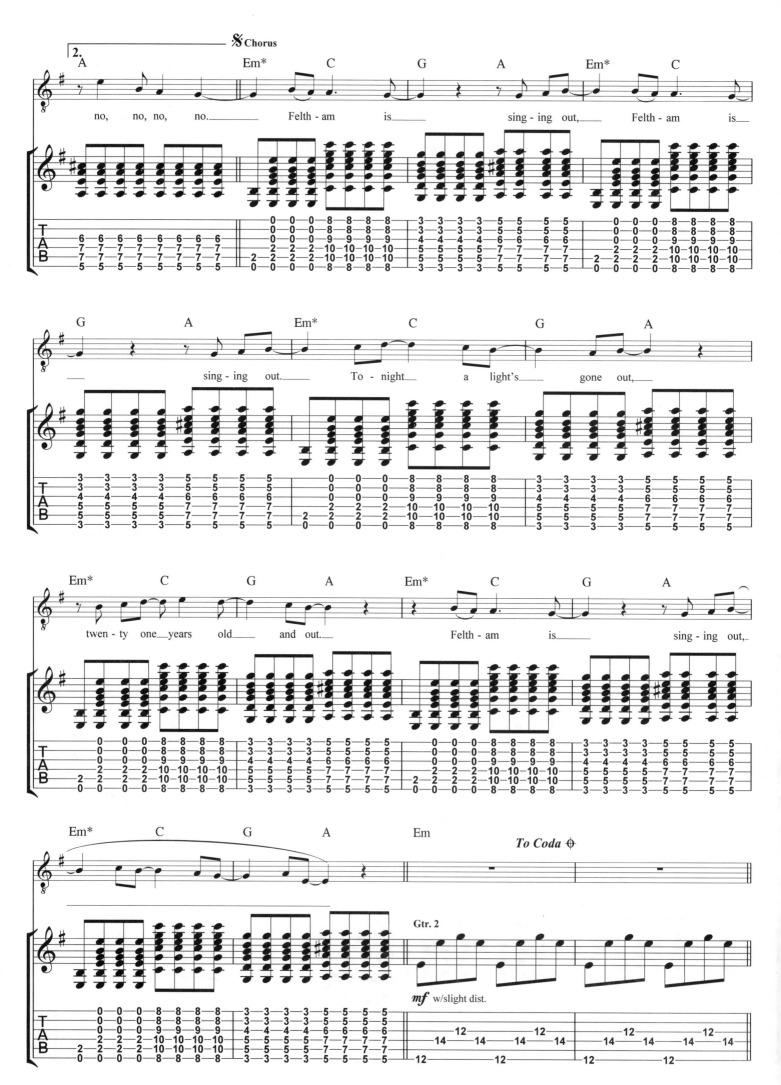

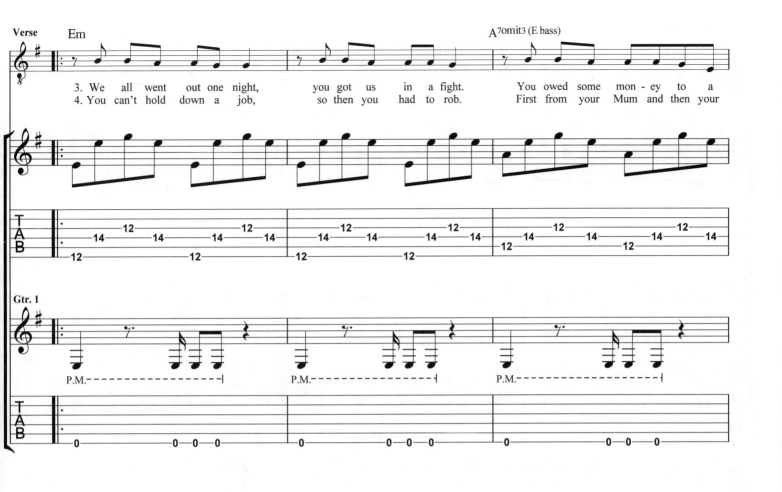

Chorus

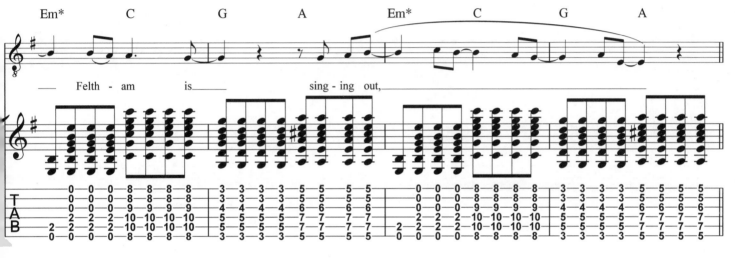

Outro

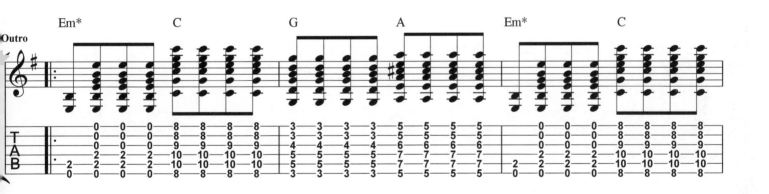

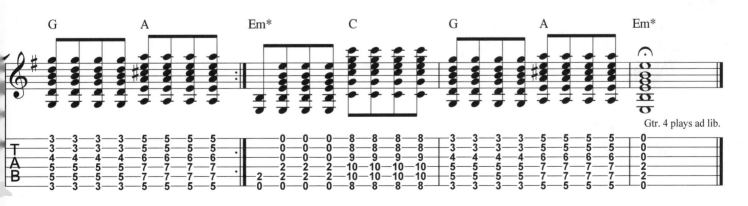

Gtr. 4 plays ad lib.

LIVING FOR THE WEEKEND

WORDS & MUSIC BY RICHARD ARCHER

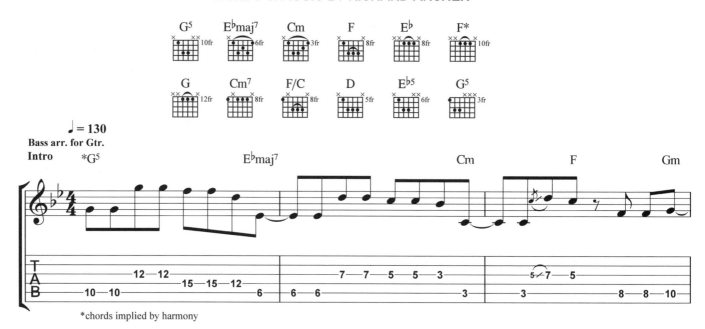

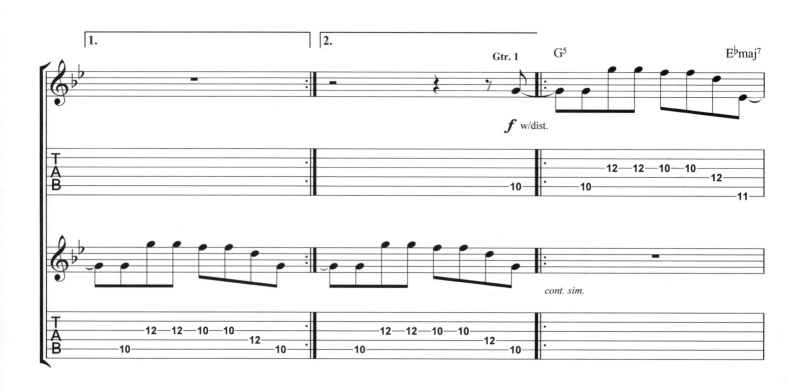

*chords implied by harmony

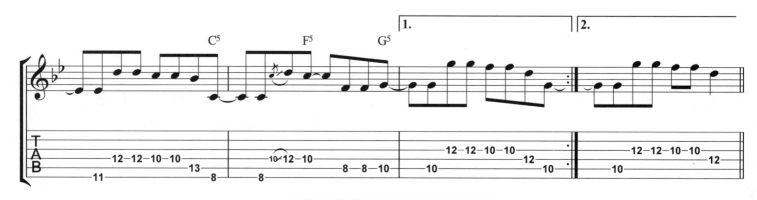

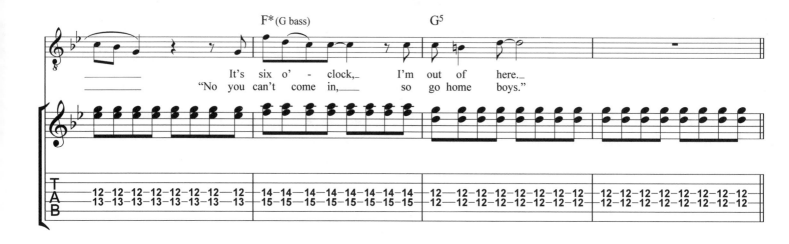

Pre-Chorus

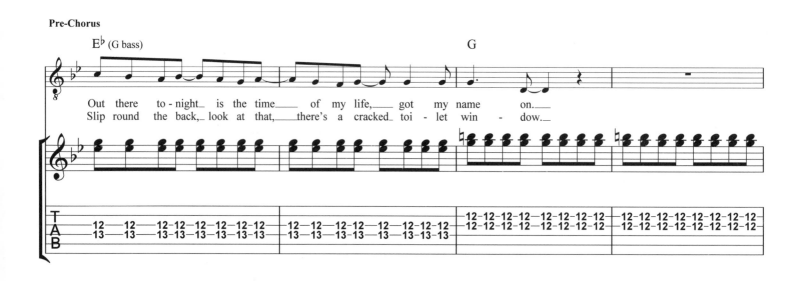

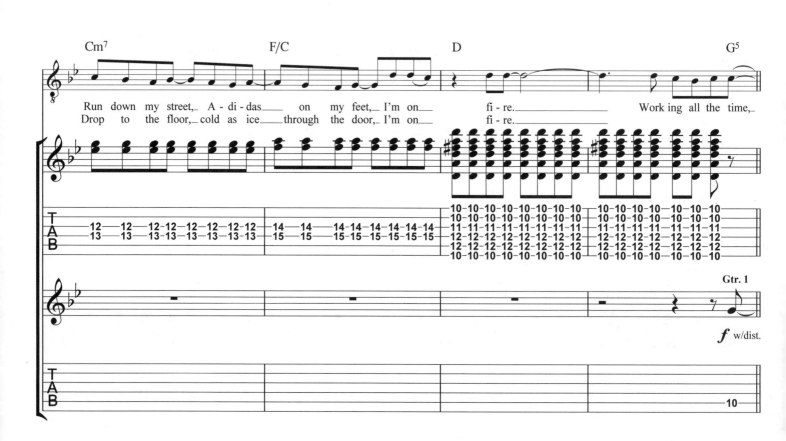

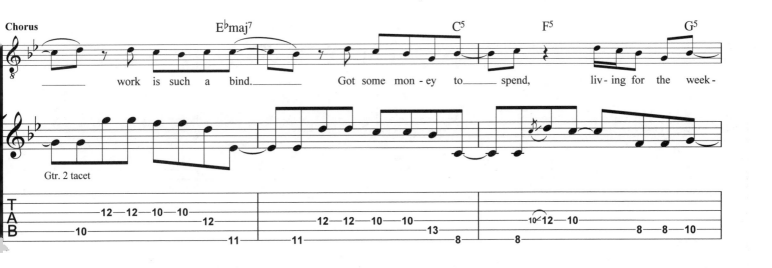

Chorus

_____ work is such a bind. _____ Got some mon - ey to _____ spend, liv - ing for the week -

Gtr. 2 tacet

- end. When it gets too much, _____ I live for the rush. _____ Got some mon - ey to _____

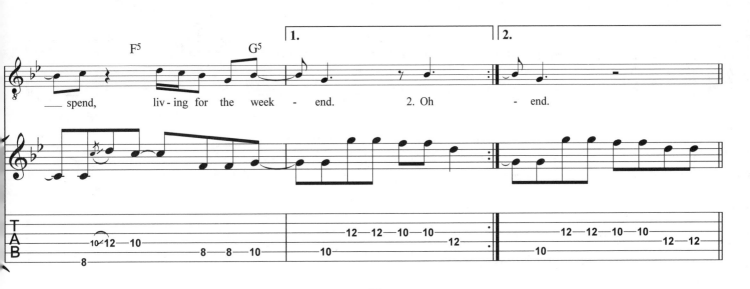

_____ spend, liv - ing for the week - end. 2. Oh - end.

71

STARS OF CCTV
WORDS & MUSIC BY RICHARD ARCHER

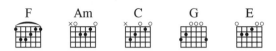

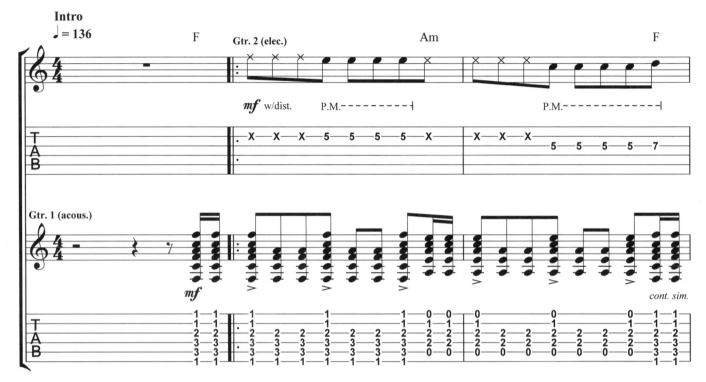

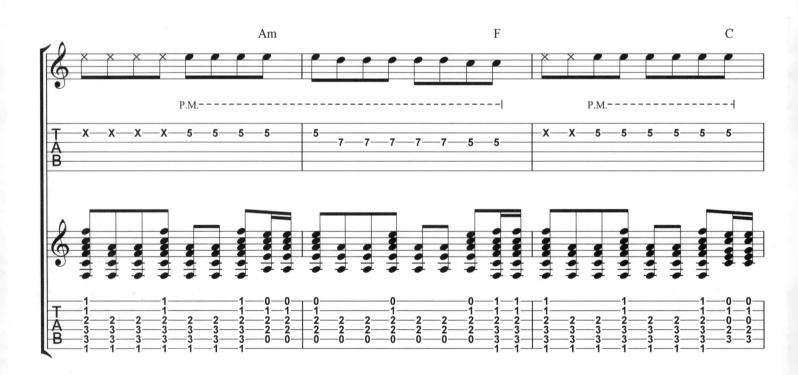

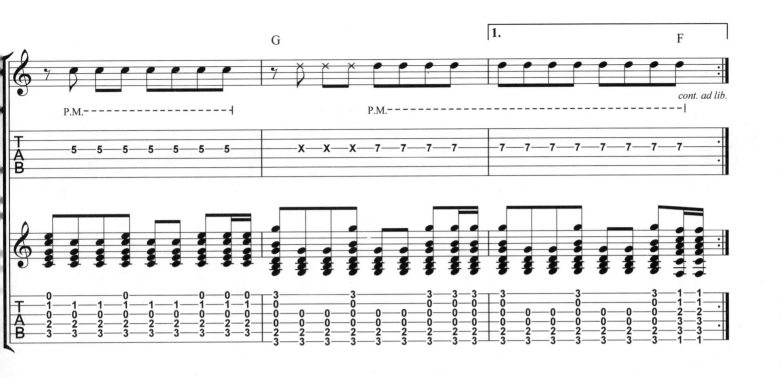

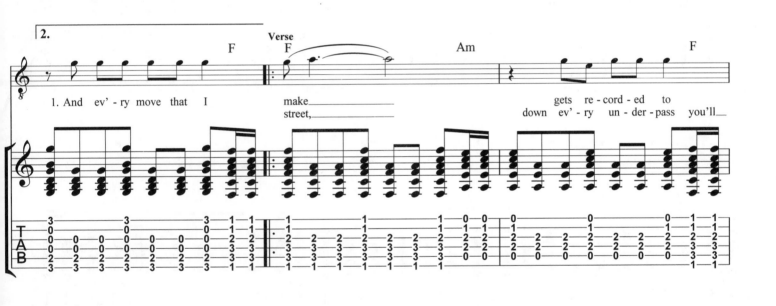

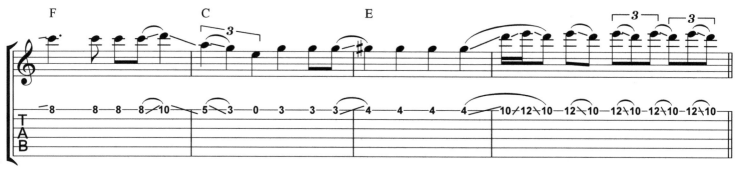

Chorus

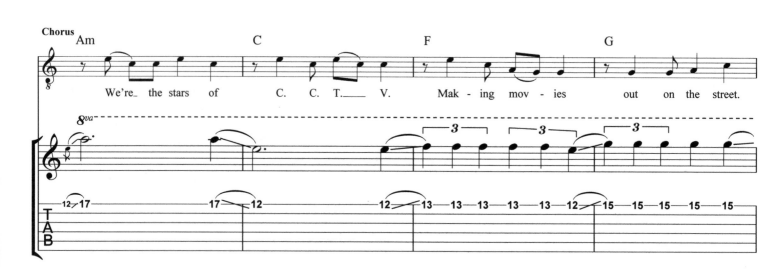

We're the stars of C. C. T. V. Mak - ing mov - ies out on the street.

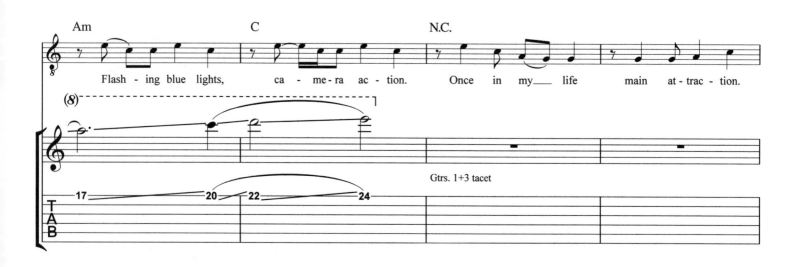

Flash - ing blue lights, ca - me - ra ac - tion. Once in my life main at - trac - tion.

Gtrs. 1+3 tacet

We're the stars of C. C. T. V. Can't you see the ca - me - ra loves me.

Guitar Tablature Explained

Guitar music can be notated in three different ways: on a musical stave, in tablature, and in rhythm slashes

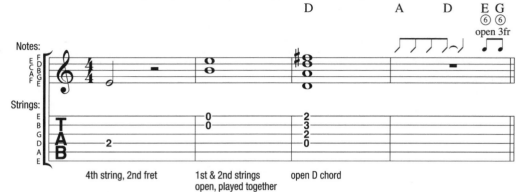

RHYTHM SLASHES are written above the stave. Strum chords in the rhythm indicated. Round noteheads indicate single notes.

THE MUSICAL STAVE shows pitches and rhythms and is divided by lines into bars. Pitches are named after the first seven letters of the alphabet.

TABLATURE graphically represents the guitar fingerboard. Each horizontal line represents a string, and each number represents a fret.

4th string, 2nd fret   1st & 2nd strings open, played together   open D chord

Definitions For Special Guitar Notation

SEMI-TONE BEND: Strike the note and bend up a semi-tone (1/2 step).

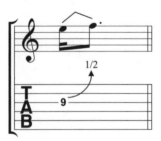

WHOLE-TONE BEND: Strike the note and bend up a whole-tone (whole step).

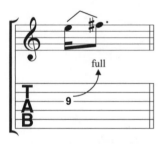

GRACE NOTE BEND: Strike the note and bend as indicated. Play the first note as quickly as possible.

QUARTER-TONE BEND: Strike the note and bend up a 1/4 step.

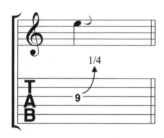

BEND & RELEASE: Strike the note and bend up as indicated, then release back to the original note.

COMPOUND BEND & RELEASE: Strike the note and bend up and down in the rhythm indicated.

PRE-BEND: Bend the note as indicated, then strike it.

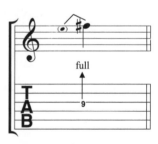

PRE-BEND & RELEASE: Bend the note as indicated. Strike it and release the note back to the original pitch.

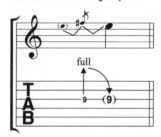

HAMMER-ON: Strike the first note with one finger, then sound the second note (on the same string) with another finger by fretting it without picking.

PULL-OFF: Place both fingers on the notes to be sounded, strike the first note and without picking, pull the finger off to sound the second note.

LEGATO SLIDE (GLISS): Strike the first note and then slide the same fret-hand finger up or down to the second note. The second note is not struck.

MUFFLED STRINGS: A percussive sound is produced by laying the fret hand across the string(s) without depressing, and striking them with the pick hand.

NATURAL HARMONIC: Strike the note while the fret-hand lightly touches the string directly over the fret indicated.

PICK SCRAPE: The edge of the pick is rubbed down (or up) the string, producing a scratchy sound.

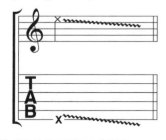

PALM MUTING: The note is partially muted by the pick hand lightly touching the string(s) just before the bridge.

SHIFT SLIDE (GLISS & RESTRIKE): Same as legato slide, except the second note is struck.

NOTE: The speed of any bend is indicated by the music notation and tempo.